Great Anteater

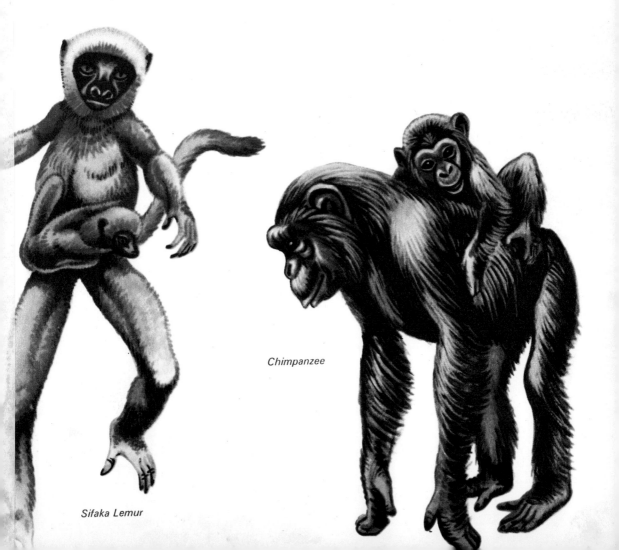

Chimpanzee

Sifaka Lemur

CONTENTS

© Odhams Books Limited 1965
Phototypeset by Oliver Burridge Filmsetting Limited, Crawley
Printed in Poland

MAMMALS

Strange and Exotic

WRITTEN AND ILLUSTRATED BY
DAVID ROOK

ODHAMS BOOKS LIMITED
LONG ACRE, LONDON

7s. 6d.

About 180 million years ago, when the great reptiles were masters of the world, the first mammals appeared.

The very first mammals closely resembled their lizard-like ancestors and had many reptilian characteristics, but certain important changes had occurred which separated the mammals forever from their predecessors. They possessed fur, they were more or less warm-blooded and they suckled their young with milk produced in their own bodies. There were other changes, but these were the main ones.

The first mammals were few and very small. The remains of a rat-sized mammal now known as *morganucodon* have been found in Wales. Probably the superior intelligence and adaptability of these first mammals enabled them to establish themselves and to spread all over the world. Their continued survival brought to an end fifty-five million years later, the great Age of Reptiles, and established the Age of Mammals.

Between these two stupendous events, the invasion of the world by these mammals was taking place, but infinitely slowly. As evolution worked its slow process of change, new species of mammals took to the forests and the dense jungles. Some learned to fly like the birds, others burrowed deep into the earth, or went back to the water from which their ancestors had appeared; others again became expert tree-climbers.

One of the species which adopted life in the treetops developed hands with which to grip the branches in which it lived. The descendants of this family increased in size, took to the ground again and gradually learned to walk upright on their hind legs.

This book is not about the familiar, but the unfamiliar, the oddities of the Animal Kingdom. Some are rare; some are comic; some are fascinatingly grotesque with habits which make us either marvel or laugh. They are all strange, and because of their peculiar qualities, undoubtedly exotic.

6

Mammals
of the forest

Mammals are very consistent in their choice of habitat or surroundings in which to live.

The *Malayan tapir* for example, whose picture you see on this page, prefers the swampy forests of its native Malaya to open grassland, and only moves about at night. Broadly speaking, mammals can be divided according to how and where they live, and this is how they are treated in this book.

These tapirs are shy, retiring mammals, browsing at night on the lush tropical vegetation that grows in the swamps and on the river-banks of their home. At first it would appear strange that such a timid defenceless creature should wear such a startling coat; but see them in their natural surroundings as they wander through patches of moonlight and their colour is a perfect camouflage. Baby tapirs are born with a completely different pattern of stripes and spots, but as they grow up they lose these "baby clothes" and develop the same markings as their parents.

A fascinating family

The mammals shown on these two pages are all related to each other, though they live in forests, in widely different parts of the world.

The two large creatures on this page, with their distinctive colouring, are both *pandas*. At the top is the *lesser panda* found high in the Himalayas, and below the *giant panda*.

The lesser panda is an attractive little animal, especially if he is out with his family. They always walk in single file through the trees. However, its claws and its fierce temper make it unsuitable as a pet!

The giant panda, one of the world's rarest mammals, is found in a small mountainous area of China where it feeds on bamboo shoots. It is the symbol of The World Wildlife Fund, a world-wide organisation dedicated to the preservation of animal life.

On this page you can see three smaller members of the family: from left to right they are the *raccoon*, the *coatimundi* and the *kinkajou*, and they all come from North and South America.

Raccoons are among the best-known mammals in America; they are found everywhere and will eat almost anything, even raiding dustbins for tit-bits. It was the unfortunate raccoon who supplied Davy Crockett with his famous hat! A raccoon will always try to wash his food thoroughly before eating, which is rather a charming and endearing habit, and one which is most amusing to witness.

Coatimundis travel through the forests in bands split into two divisions: one division travels through the treetops, while the other follows on the ground picking up any fruit or insects that are knocked down by their friends up above.

Kinkajous come out at night and will eat almost anything they can find but they are especially fond of honey.

Mammals that live in the open air

Now we come to another species of mammal—the kind that lives in open country. Mammals of the woodlands can escape their enemies in the dense undergrowth, or climb rapidly up trees, but those who live in the open must rely upon other means of protection. Some rely on swift flight, while others have protective shells like the fantastic *armadillo* family of Central and South America. The *nine-banded armadillo*, on the left, has a flexible shell made partly of horn and partly of bone. When frightened, it rolls up into a tight ball, so that all its soft underparts are hidden, or it digs itself into the ground with amazing speed, using its powerful claws. These armadillos, also known as "titus", bear four young, and these are always either four males or four females.

The *giant armadillo*, below, is really a forest-dweller, but has similar habits to its cousins. The eight-inch claws on its forelegs are the biggest of any mammal; it has more teeth (up to 90) than any other mammal, with the exception of some of the whales.

The tiny *fairy armadillo* of Argentina and Bolivia, which is only six inches long, is surely one of the strangest of the family. This elusive, fascinating creature is a beautiful pink all over, with long silvery hair on its face and belly. It

burrows continually after insects and grubs, and in cold weather it stays underground. The stiff tail is used to prop up the end of its body when it is digging: this leaves the hind legs free to churn away the earth loosened by the strong front claws.

As you can see in the picture, the back end of the fairy armadillo is almost squared-off, and covered by a solid horny plate. There is a reason for this: if caught in the open, the fairy armadillo can dig a hole with lightning speed, dive in and leave its solid backside plugging the entrance!

A close relative of the armadillo family is the *great anteater*, also of South America. Like the armadillo it feeds on ants and termites, using its powerful forelegs with their curved claws to rip open rotting logs and even sun-baked termites' nests to get inside.

Sometimes it uses its long bushy tail like a broom to sweep the tiny insects into a neat pile before eating them. This tail has more than one use, for when the anteater curls up for its day's rest, in the shelter of the undergrowth, it carefully covers itself with its tail, which thus serves either as a sunshade or as a warm blanket, according to the time of year. The great anteater is a friendly, harmless creature and bothers nobody as it wanders about in search of ants, but if it is attacked it quickly proves that it is not the clown it might appear: standing up on its hind legs, supporting itself with its tail, it spreads its forelegs wide and faces the enemy fearlessly. It can move like lightning, inflicting terrible wounds with its huge claws.

Although the great anteater lives on land, it is an excellent swimmer, and is able to cross even very wide rivers.

A mother anteater has one baby a year and from its birth she carries it on her back, as you will see if you look at the drawings inside the cover. The baby anteater enjoys riding on Mother's back so much that it stays there for a whole year; until, in fact, the next baby arrives, when it must leave.

11

A long neck can be useful

Two of these mammals have become specially adapted to their life on the plains; the *giraffe*, and, in the centre, the little *gerenuk*.

The giraffe's enormously long legs and neck enable it to browse on leaves at the very top of the trees found on the plains of Africa. He does this when all the lower leaves have been eaten by the many other forms of hoofed mammal that live side by side with him.

This "specialisation" has allowed the giraffe to survive when other, shorter-necked mammals died out from lack of food aeons ago. Such "specialisation", however, has its disadvantages. If you have ever watched a giraffe trying to drink, you must have noticed how he has to

straddle his front legs in a most ungainly way for
his head to reach down far enough to the water.
If the giraffe is caught in this position he cannot
defend himself.

The rare, delicate gerenuk, found between
Abyssinia and Tanganyika, is a gazelle, but like
the giraffe it has developed long legs and a long
neck which enable it to reach up into the trees, as
you can see.

The strange creature on the right is another
rarity; it is an *okapi*, related to the giraffe, and
not actually discovered until early this century.
Unlike the giraffe, it lives in the depths of the
forests of the Congo, but I have included it here
as it is truly one of the oddities of the Animal
Kingdom, with its weird colouring and shy
habits.

13

Here are two more mammals with special adaptations for life in the open; both are members of the dog tribe.

Above is the dainty *fennec*, or *bat-eared fox*, of North Africa and Arabia. This little creature, with its very long ears, hunts at night for small mammals, birds, reptiles and insects, relying more on its highly developed hearing than on its sight which is not very good.

The peculiar *maned wolf*, which lives on the grassy pampas of Brazil, Paraguay and Argentina, is much less known, and is comparatively rare.

This is another of the mammals that The World Wildlife Fund is attempting to preserve. The maned wolf hunts, mostly at night, for the same kind of food as the fennec fox, although it eats a greater proportion of small mammals. If the cheetah is one of the fastest runners of the Animal Kingdom, the maned wolf must be a close second for it can average a speed of nearly fifty miles an hour.

Also very fast is the *jerboa*, found over much of Asia and in North Africa, but this animal uses its kangaroo-like hind legs to leap along, as you can see from the picture below.

Jerboas come out mostly at night to feed on insects and desert plants, and can be seen in their millions after rain when the deserts in which they live teem with life for a short while. Some species go into a kind of sleep when food is short, and wake up again when conditions are more favourable. They are easily tamed and make good pets. When in captivity, jerboas develop a positive passion for any sort of broom, and if allowed will actually make a nest amongst the bristles!

The other small mammal shown here is the *elephant-shrew*, of which many kinds are to be found in Africa. Its strange name stems from its mobile, trunk-like nose, with which it probes into nooks and crannies for insects and grubs. It is not at all elephant-like, however, when it is frightened, for it will disappear from sight with huge leaps, leaving behind it a cloud of dust. Some observers have reported that these elephant-shrews escape downhill by curling themselves up into balls and rolling away.

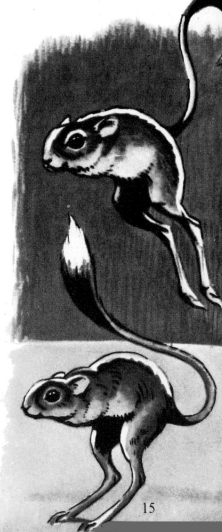

Mammal beauty parade

Here are three of the strangest faces in the mammal kingdom.

The first belongs to the *naked mole rat*, or *sand puppy*, which burrows in the burning sands of the deserts of Somaliland, in Africa. It has the same kind of habits as the *English mole*, except that it eats roots as well as insects and grubs. It has no external ears, tiny lidless eyes, and only a few scattered hairs on its body.

The second belongs to an animal common over much of Africa—the *wart hog*. It uses its long tusks to grub up the roots and tubers which form a large part of its diet. Wart hogs travel in herds, and if disturbed trot away with tails held straight up in the air, which makes them look more ridiculous than ever. If they stampede they often trample over one another in their panic.

The last of the oddities is the quaint little *star-nosed mole* of Eastern North America. Unlike the sand puppy, the star-nosed mole enjoys cool, moist places. It uses its strange nose and its fleshy, sensitive fingers when searching in the moist earth for food.

16

The legend of the lemmings

One of the best-known of the animal legends relates how every few years the *lemmings* of Norway gather together and move in their millions to the coast, where they swim out to sea and drown.

This is not quite accurate for in a "Lemming Year", not all the lemmings join this suicidal march. Some remain behind in the mountains and seem entirely unaware of the mass migration of their relatives.

The millions who do set out for the sea on their last journey sometimes never reach it, for many thousands become casualties; some are killed on the way by foxes, hawks and owls, or else they are run over by cars or drowned in rivers. In fact only a fraction of the original millions finally reach the sea. The strangest part of the lemming story, however, is not told in the legend. Some of these wanderers actually stop and settle by the wayside. At first all goes well and they start to breed, but after a while the old lemmings die, and the young ones move on. Thus, no new colony is ever formed.

The strange creature on the left, in its armour plating, is the *pangolin* of Africa, another mammal that feeds on ants and termites. Apart from its appearance, it has the peculiar habit of sleeping in the position shown here.

17

Mammals that live in the water

Many mammals are proficient swimmers and find most of their food in the water, but some have actually made the water their home. All water-living mammals breathe air, including whales, and must be able to surface, otherwise they will drown just like any land-living mammal. The great *seal* family are descendants of dog-like flesh-eating mammals that gradually took to the water millions of years ago. Now their limbs have become flippers and they are superb swimmers.

The seal that is diving off the rock in the drawing is a *grey seal* which is quite common around the coasts of Britain.

18

The strange bloated seal at the top of the opposite page is an *elephant seal* or *sea elephant*, so called because of its trunk; this trunk normally hangs down over the mouth, as in the picture. When the sea elephant is angry or excited, however, he inflates his nose so that it swells up over his head. An angry bull sea elephant, which can be as long as eighteen feet and fifteen feet round the middle, is an awe-inspiring sight.

At the bottom of the opposite page is the familiar *walrus,* found in the Arctic Ocean. Although the walrus is not so vast as the sea elephant, big males can measure twelve feet long and weigh up to a ton and a half.

At the top of this page is a typical baby seal in his warm woolly coat of white fur. His large liquid eyes and almost human crying make him one of the most attractive of all baby animals.

Below is a mother *dolphin* with her baby. Many people do not realise that dolphins, *porpoises* and *whales* are as much mammals as dogs and cats. Not only are they true mammals, but they are far more intelligent than most.

The friendly creature on the left is the *manatee*, found around the coasts of America and on the West Coast of Africa, and often travelling hundreds of miles up the larger rivers. Manatees live in groups and browse on various water plants using their cleft upper lips to seize their food and stuff it into their mouths. At night they often make a moaning noise, for no apparent reason, and this sound, coupled with the fact that they sometimes hold their babies in their arms to suckle them, may have given rise to the mermaid legends.

A related and similar mammal, the *dugong,* has been exterminated in many parts of the world by men, who hunt and kill it for its oil and its flesh.

The *sea otter*, above, is another fascinating creature that has been hunted by man until its existence is in danger. A distant relative of the *British otter*, sea otters spend nearly all their lives at sea. They feed on all kinds of sea life, often diving to fantastic depths for shellfish. When they are feeding they float on their backs, as you see in the picture, and hold their food in their forepaws; they will play for hours with shells or pieces of seaweed in this position.

Mammals that live in trees

We have seen how mammals adapt themselves to their surroundings. We move on now to those mammals which are especially suited to life in the treetops.

All such tree-climbing animals must have either long muscular tails which act as additional supports, or *hands*, as opposed to paws. Ground-living mammals have either paws, or hooves, but these would be useless among the slender, often slippery, branches of trees.

Consequently, those mammals which took to the trees developed digits ("fingers" or "toes") which are "opposable"; that is to say, which bend in the opposite direction to the other digits. Perhaps this will be easier to understand when you realise that your thumb is "opposable" to your fingers. When you grip an object, your thumb curls round it in the opposite direction to your fingers, enabling you to take a firm hold.

Hands of apes and monkeys are mostly similar to your own, as you can see if you look carefully at the picture of the *orang-utan*. This large and most intelligent ape is found in the jungles of Borneo and Sumatra: its name means "wild man of the woods". It is yet another in the long list of mammals in danger of extinction and is in need of man's protection.

21

The monkey family

The *woolly monkey* from South America, in the bottom left-hand corner, is one of the least temperamental of the monkey tribe, and for this reason it makes a very good pet.

Above the woolly monkey is a *grey gibbon*. These apes are found in the forests of Indonesia and Southern Asia and are most agile.

The monkey beside him with the preposterous nose is the *proboscis monkey* from Borneo. Only the male has this remarkable nose, although the females and their young have rather comical faces. They are powerful swimmers, and will cross wide stretches of water—a most unusual feat for a monkey. They will also dive underwater to hide from enemies.

Just above, a *spider monkey* is having his tail pulled by a *colobus monkey* from Africa. Notice how the spider monkey's prehensile tail grips the twig for extra support. These monkeys no longer possess thumbs; they hang from branches as opposed to gripping them. Groups of spider monkeys hanging by their tails and casually using their hands to pick fruit are an amusing sight.

The startling silky coats of the colobus monkeys have almost been their downfall, for these can be fashioned into brilliant clothing and decoration. In some areas, these monkeys have been almost completely wiped out.

The *golden* or *silky marmosets* are small relatives of colobus monkeys, living in the South American forests where they sleep in tree hollows, tightly packed together.

23

Here are two mammals which do not possess opposable thumbs. The strange creature hanging upside down is a *sloth*, of a variety known as an "*ai*". This sloth has three clawed toes on its front legs: another variety has only two claws, and both species live in South America. Sloths, in fact, spend almost the whole of their lives upside down, clinging to tree branches and feeding on leaves, young shoots and fruits. If a sloth has to descend to the ground it is at a loss and almost completely helpless. On page 37, you will see how a mother sloth carries her baby until it is big enough to look after itself. The sloth dislikes action and moves only when necessary.

The second mammal on this page is the *tamandua*, or *lesser anteater*, closely related to the great anteater on page 11. The tamandua eats ants and termites, but unlike its cousin it concentrates on tree-nesting insects. Notice how the powerful prehensile tail steadies it while it prepares to rip away a large piece of bark with its powerful claws. When attacked on the ground the tamandua stands erect and slashes out with its dangerous claws which can inflict severe wounds.

The world's noisiest mammals

The appropriately named *howler monkeys* live in the depths of the forests of South America. Led by a big male, they move about in bands, and feed on leaves.

Sometimes two different bands of howlers meet in the treetops. With many animals this would mean a struggle for supremacy. The howlers, however, do not resort to physical violence. Instead, they start howling. The noise is unbelievable and quite unforgettable, carrying for miles in the still air. It is kept up for perhaps ten minutes, until it is quite clear that one band is making more noise than the other, and is therefore a bigger group. The smaller band then moves quietly and peaceably out of the way in an admission of defeat, but it has been a bloodless battle!

This amazing howl, which is sometimes like a lion's roar or distant thunder, even an elephant trumpeting in pain, is produced in a special spherical voice-box. It must surely be the loudest sound made by any mammal, or indeed by any animal on earth!

The common *opossum* of North America also spends nearly all its life in trees. Its "hands" are not quite as human in appearance as those of the monkeys, but they grip just as efficiently. The opossum is a marsupial (like the mammals of Australia), although it does not possess a pouch as most of the Australian marsupials do. An opossum will sometimes give birth to as many as eighteen young, but is unable to carry all these and abandons some immediately. The remaining babies cling onto mother's back until they are well grown, and must be a heavy burden for her to carry.

You may have heard the expression "playing possum". It is derived from the opossum's habit of apparently fainting and lying still when danger threatens.

Notice, again, the strong prehensile tail gripping the branch. Without this fifth hand, mother opossum could hardly keep her balance.

Another useful tail belongs to the dumpy little *coendou*, or *hairy tree porcupine* from Brazil and Paraguay. Like all porcupines it has bristles, but these are hidden under the thick fur. If cornered, the coendou will stand erect and put up its fists like a boxer, doing its best to give a very fierce growl; it is, however, a peaceful creature, and it makes a wonderful and fascinating pet.

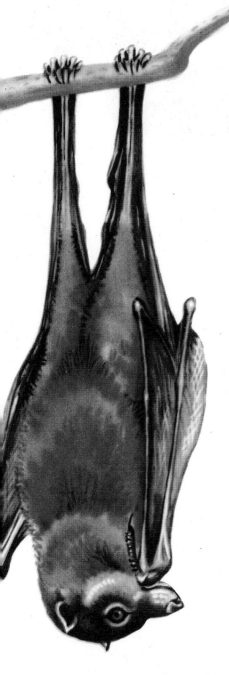

Mammals that fly

Perhaps the most amazing accomplishment in the history of the mammal kingdom occurred when mammals learned to fly. Taking to the trees or even to the water did not involve too much adaptation, but for flying—you must have some kind of wings.

Many millions of years ago, a family of small shrew-like creatures managed to develop leathery wings, just as did certain lizards millions of years before that. These winged mammals we now know as bats. Fossil remains of bats have been found which are fifty-five million years old, and there were certainly bats a long time before that.

Bats are found over most of the world, and can be divided generally into two classes: the big fruit-eaters, like the *flying fox* drawn here, and the small insect-eaters like the bats on the next page. They are well-known for their common habit of roosting by day in caves or old buildings, where they hang upside down by the claws of their hind legs, packed together like sardines in a tin. In one enormous cave in Texas, the number of bats sleeping there in one day was estimated at something near twenty million!

Perhaps the most interesting fact about bats is the manner in which they find their way in the dark and catch their food. As they fly they emit incredibly high-pitched squeaks through their nostrils. If any object is in their path, this sound bounces off it and returns to the bat as an echo. The echo is picked up by the bat's amazingly sensitive ears and the bat can then avoid the obstacle, or if it happens to be a flying insect, catch it.

27

The two insect-eating bats drawn above have bodies only a few inches long. While most bats are a uniform brown or grey in colour, these two are somewhat brighter and more attractive in appearance.

The bat on the left is the *red bat* from North America, a close cousin to the commonest English bat, the little *pipistrelle*.

The one on the right is a *painted bat* from Africa, surely the prettiest of all bats with its mouse-like head and body and its delicately patterned wings. No wonder it is also known as the *butterfly bat*.

At the other end of the scale are some of the most monstrous and ridiculous faces of the whole animal kingdom. The *naked bat* (top right) is found in Malaya and Borneo. In appearance it looks somewhat like a bloated pig, and its almost hairless skin is folded and wrinkled. It has a pouch on its chest which may be used for carrying its young while in flight, though this is not very certain.

The bat with the face like that of a sad horse (centre right) is the weird *hammer-headed bat* from West Africa. Its head is so big that it hangs down when the bat is flying.

The *great horseshoe bat* (bottom right) is one species which you might know for it is found over much of the world, including Britain.

Although bats are the only mammals that can actually fly, other species have learned to glide or parachute.

Whereas a bat can fly upwards as well as downwards, gliding mammals can only take off from a tall tree and glide downwards to another tree. In order to be able to do this, they have developed a fold of skin which can be stretched out when the limbs are extended. If you think of a paper dart you will perhaps get the idea more clearly.

The two pictures on this page, of a North American *flying squirrel*, show how this flap of skin folds between the front and back legs when the animal is climbing; and then how it stretches out as it begins to glide.

The flying squirrel uses its long bushy tail like a rudder to steer it in its flight, and to help it to land on the tree of its choice. Without this "rudder", the flight would most probably have a disastrous ending, for the poor flying squirrel might easily find himself going head-first into a solid tree or dropping straight down into the open mouth of some waiting hungry fox.

29

Night gliders

This strange mammal (above) is indeed an oddity, for it belongs to a unique group and has not a single relative. It is a *cobego*, or *colugo*. In fact, there are many ways of spelling its name, and these are just two of them!

The cobego is found in Malaya, Siam, Sumatra, Borneo, Java and the Philippines. By day it sleeps in a way which is altogether remarkable, for it hangs upside down by all four feet, and tucks its head and tail inside its legs. The effect is rather like a brown shopping bag which has somehow been suspended from a branch.

At night the cobego glides from tree to tree in search of food. It eats fruit and leaves, and, because it has more extensive gliding membranes than any other gliding mammal, it can cover long distances on its food-hunting expeditions. Cobegos have been seen to glide as far as two hundred feet.

The female gives birth to one offspring which is small and naked at first, and for some time after it is born, clings onto its mother's stomach or chest— even when she is in flight.

30

Both the creatures on this page are marsupials from Australia, and both are tiny. The one gliding with its baby on its back is the pretty *sugar glider* or *sugar-squirrel*, and there is another picture of it on the left.

These mammals clamber about the trees and bushes by night in search of flowers, leaves and insects, and are especially fond of honey or nectar, hence the name, sugar-glider.

By the day they sleep curled up in little groups in nests of leaves which they make in hollow trees. Although they appear gentle, they fight among themselves, and make a surprising amount of noise for such tiny animals. If the sugar-gliders are disturbed in their daytime nest, they will leap out and glide rapidly away, looking rather like a shower of wind-blown snowflakes or petals, but moving much faster!

The other glider, which I have drawn sitting on a human hand, is the *pigmy flying opossum*, and you can see how tiny they are.

They have smaller gliding membranes, and cannot glide very fast; their tails, however, are most delicate rudders, and look just like feathers. This feathery tail gives the opossum his alternative name, *gliding feather-tails*.

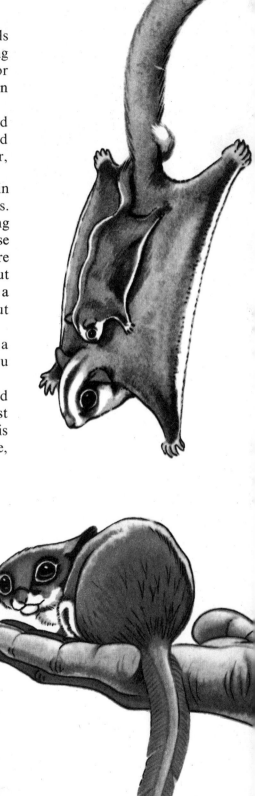

Mammals of the night

Take a clearing in the depths of the South American jungle. At midday make a list of all the mammals to be seen and heard. If you return to that same clearing at midnight, twelve hours later, the chances are that not one mammal on your daytime list will be found. Instead there will be a completely new set of mammals there, searching for food. Most mammals you see are active either in the daytime or at night. Very few mammals are active both in the daytime and at night. We have seen how most tree-living mammals have grasping hands or tails to help them. Mammals which use the night hours for hunting nearly always have big eyes, and often big ears as well.

The rat-sized *tarsier* is a very good example of a nocturnal mammal. Its huge eyes enable it to see the night-flying moths and other insects on which it feeds, and these it catches expertly with its hands.

The mammal below the tarsier is a *slow loris*, from Indonesia. The name "loris" comes from a word meaning "clown", and you can see why this is such a good name. The slow loris moves about with incredible slowness eating vegetable food and large insects which it catches by creeping up on them.

Above and to the right is a cousin of the slow loris: this is the *slender loris* of India and Ceylon. It is undoubtedly a little faster in its movements than its relative, but this does not mean much for it is still painfully slow. It eats less fruit and more insects than the slow loris and is said to creep up on sleeping birds and strangle them. It is very small, being only about five inches long.

The last mammal on this page is the pretty little *douroucouli* or *night-monkey* of South America. It has striking pure-white eyebrows over its huge eyes, and is altogether a beautiful creature to look at, although it can be rather short tempered.

Above is the *aye-aye*, and this is among the strangest of the mammals. It belongs to the *lemur* tribe, and like most lemurs is found only on the Island of Madagascar.

It has a varied diet, feeding happily on insects, small mammals and birds, fruits, and the pith of bamboo and cane which is readily to hand.

The aye-aye was once believed to be a rodent, like a rabbit or a rat, because of its rodent-like front teeth, but it has now been found to be a primitive lemur, though it bears no resemblance to any of its distant cousins.

One of the oddest things about the aye-aye is the specially adapted finger on its forepaw. If you study the picture below, you will see how incredibly thin it is and how it ends in a curved claw.

There are conflicting opinions as to the use of this claw, but most people agree that the aye-aye uses his claw to extract pith from bamboo stems and insects and grubs from crevices in tree barks.

Some observers claim, however, that this claw is simply used for tapping on the barks of trees in order to frighten the insects into leaving their hiding-place. When they appear, the aye-aye catches them. But this does not seem quite such a plausible theory.

The female aye-aye builds a large nest in which she has her single baby.

Both this creature and the one on the next page are becoming more and more rare, and at least one kind of Madagascan lemur is on the verge of extinction.

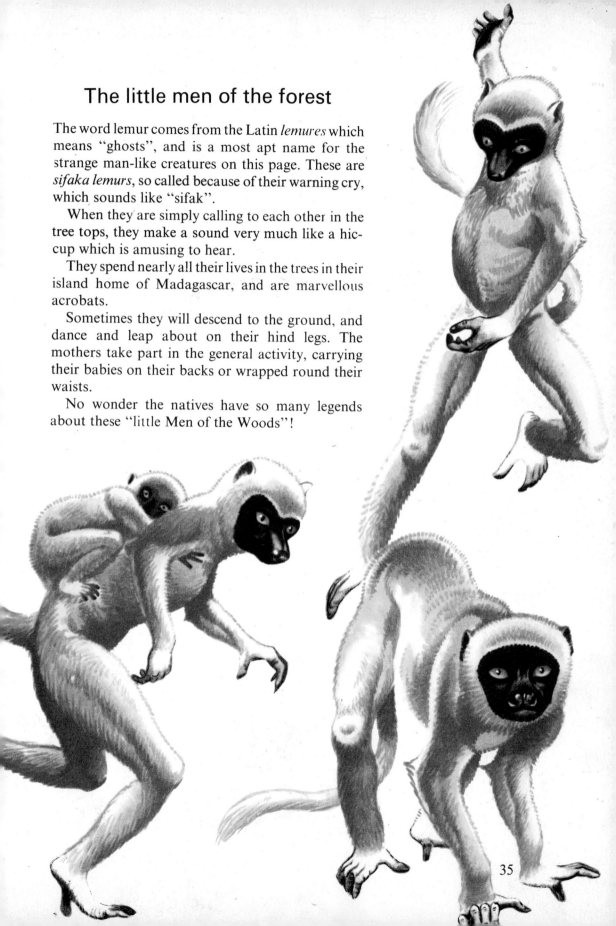

The little men of the forest

The word lemur comes from the Latin *lemures* which means "ghosts", and is a most apt name for the strange man-like creatures on this page. These are *sifaka lemurs*, so called because of their warning cry, which sounds like "sifak".

When they are simply calling to each other in the tree tops, they make a sound very much like a hiccup which is amusing to hear.

They spend nearly all their lives in the trees in their island home of Madagascar, and are marvellous acrobats.

Sometimes they will descend to the ground, and dance and leap about on their hind legs. The mothers take part in the general activity, carrying their babies on their backs or wrapped round their waists.

No wonder the natives have so many legends about these "little Men of the Woods"!

35

Of ants and elephants

We have already seen the strange cobego, which has no relatives on earth, and is unique in the Animal Kingdom. Here is another odd mammal, the *aard-vark*.

This peculiar creature is found over much of Africa, and has a comical appearance with its long nose and donkey-ears. It is a powerful creature, growing, at times, to a length of six feet, but it requires all its strength to break open the huge termite nests so as to reach the insects on which it feeds. These termite nests are sometimes twenty feet tall, and a man with a pick-axe would scarcely be able to make a dent in their sides.

The attractive creatures at the top of the page do have relatives, but can you guess the identity of their closest cousins? This is not as easy as you might think, for the *hyrax* is related neither to the rabbit nor to the shrew, as you might think! Although it grows no bigger than eighteen inches, its nearest relative is—the elephant! It is an excellent climber of rocks and trees.

How mammals
protect themselves

Broadly speaking, mammals can be divided into two kinds: those that kill other mammals for food, and those that do not.

The ones that kill have sharp teeth and claws; they are either strong and swift, or very cunning.

Those that do not kill and have neither sharp teeth nor claws are nevertheless capable of surviving because they have various effective ways of protecting themselves. Many such mammals, of course, do fall victim to the carnivores or flesh-eating animals, but nevertheless, numbers survive because of their camouflage or speed or cunning habits.

Camouflage is a word which means "protective colouring", and the two mammals on this page are both employing this device in order to blend into their surroundings, and so become difficult to spot. The *bushbuck*, on the right, has stripes and dashes of white which to an enemy, look like flecks of sunlight as it stands motionless in the shadows.

The *sloth* (above) has a unique method of hiding itself: the hairs of its coat are full of little holes, and in these holes grow very tiny plants called algae. In the rainy season, these tiny plants grow, and the sloth then appears green! This

green blends perfectly with the surrounding foliage, and the sloth is most effectively camouflaged.

Many hoofed mammals, deer, antelope, zebra and so on, rely on their ability to run when danger threatens. Some, such as the *gazelle* drawn below, are able to bound away in fantastically long leaps which soon carry them out of danger, unless, of course, they are taken by surprise.

The little *red squirrel*, top centre, relies on its superb agility to outwit its enemies. It runs and leaps among the topmost branches of the trees where it performs incredible acrobatic feats with a grace which is delightful to watch.

The *prairie dog*, on the left, has neither speed nor agility with which to outwit his enemies, but he does have a special kind of retreat. Prairie dogs live together in great communities, or "cities", in North America. Each family has its own burrow leading to living quarters beneath the ground, and here they are fairly safe from attack. The threat to their lives comes when they are out in the open searching for food.

In order to minimize this hazard, there are prairie dog sentries posted at strategic points fairly close to the burrows, who keep a look out for marauding hawks or coyotes, the prairie dog's two principal enemies. When a sentry is put on the alert, he gives a sharp warning bark, which sounds very similar to a dog's bark, and in an instant every prairie dog in sight has disappeared down his burrow.

The prairie dog lives on green vegetation, but in a bad season he will dig down and eat roots.

Spines, shells and smells

The *porcupine*'s method of defence is obvious. Its sharp quills are even more harmful than they appear, for as soon as they penetrate the skin of an enemy, they break off and begin to work their way inward, causing great pain or even death to the victim.

We have already seen pictures of armadillos at the beginning of the book. This one is rolled up into a tight ball. Once an armadillo has retired beneath his armour-plated covering, very few animals are strong enough to break through his defence.

Another ingenious way by which animals protect themselves from their enemies is by giving out a strong and most objectionable smell.

When the *American skunk* is threatened by danger, he immediately does a handstand and dances up and down on his forepaws; if his attacker is not deterred, he then squirts evil-smelling fluid with deadly aim, and in face of this, even a bear beats a hasty retreat!

The incredible mammals of Australia

I have left the last few pages of my book for the mammals of Australia because in every way they are unique. For millions of years the animal life of the continent of Australia and New Guinea has developed on its own, and owes nothing to outside influences. Australian mammals are, therefore, completely different from all but a very few mammals of the rest of the world. All the mammals found in Australia are marsupials; that is to say, they have pouches in which their young spend their early days. Some babies, like the young *kangaroo* opposite, will stay in Mother's pouch until he has outgrown it. Others, too, cling to this mode of transport long after they are capable of making their own way, which makes us feel sorry for the mother who must bear the weight of her increasingly heavy offspring.

The two kangaroos shown here are (left) the *red kangaroo*, and (above) the *grey kangaroo*, who can be as much as seven feet high when standing erect on his hind legs.

In countries where there are vast expanses of grassland, there are usually large numbers of hoofed mammals. These feed on the grass and act as most efficient lawnmowers. Probably you have seen on films zebra and antelope which graze across the plains of Africa. But in Australia there are no hoofed mammals. It is the kangaroos which wander about in large herds, and feed on the grass. A herd of frightened kangaroos bounding away on their powerful hind legs at a terrific speed is a thrilling, unforgettable sight.

The strange little *marsupial mole*, on the right, has no visible eyes and only minute ears. Despite these two grave disadvantages, however, it is an expert excavator. Most of its life is spent tunnelling furiously through the sands of the Australian deserts, feeding on insects and grubs as it goes. When it has eaten enough it falls fast asleep, but wakes again to search for more food.

41

Mammals that lay eggs

The most primitive mammals on earth are the mammals that lay eggs, and they are the oddest. The *duck-billed platypus* (below) is a small rounded mammal with a flattened tail, large webbed feet and the most preposterous appendage on its nose in the form of a beak made of a strong leathery substance. It lives by rivers in its Australian home, diving for fresh-water shell-fish and worms. It digs a very long burrow in the bank which has a concealed entrance under water. In this burrow the female lays two eggs whose shells are soft and rubbery. She stays with the eggs and incubates them like a hen until they hatch.

The male platypus has a kind of spur on the inside of each ankle. These spurs are connected to poison glands in the upper leg. In the mating season fighting goes on between rival males, and it is thought these spurs are used then as weapons. The spurs will certainly inflict a nasty wound on any human being who happens to get in the way of them.

. The *spiny echidna* (above) also lays an egg, but unlike the platypus, it puts the egg into its pouch where it eventually hatches. Very quaint to watch, it shuffles about on its tummy, and licks up ants with its tube-like tongue. Both the echidna and the platypus are less warm-blooded than any other mammal, and in many respects are half-way between mammals and reptiles.

One of the best known and best loved mammals in the world is the *koala bear*.

Although it looks so much like a small cuddly bear, it is not a bear at all, but a true marsupial. Its entire life is spent in the eucalyptus trees, which provide all the nourishment it needs in the shape of leaves.

The female gives birth to one or two young, which spend six months in the pouch, and then a further year on the mother's back. Indeed, by the time they leave this familiar perch, they are almost as big as their mother, who must surely be relieved to find herself free from such a burden.

When a baby koala misbehaves, Mother turns it over and spanks its bottom with her open hand. The baby gives out heart-rending screams, which she wisely ignores.

43

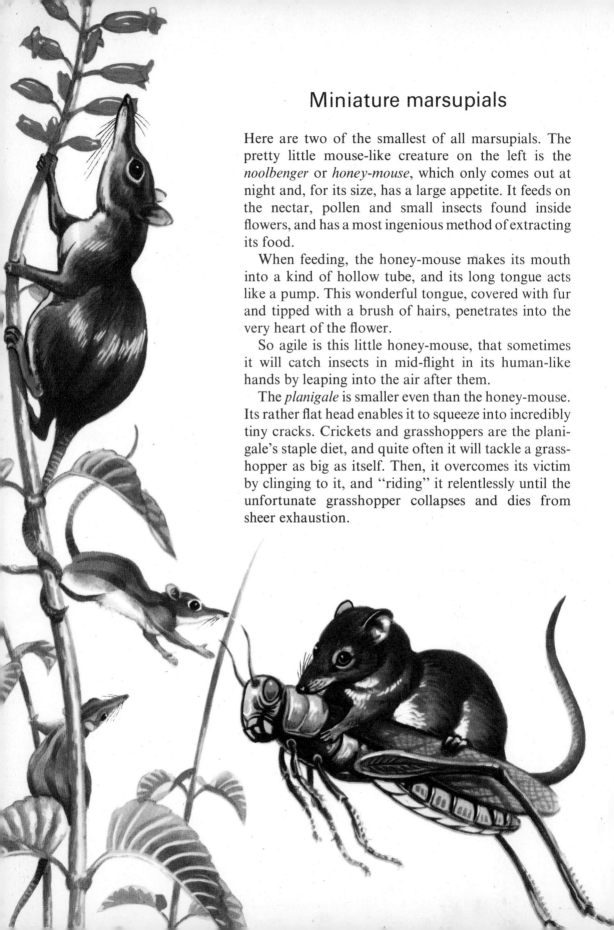

Miniature marsupials

Here are two of the smallest of all marsupials. The pretty little mouse-like creature on the left is the *noolbenger* or *honey-mouse*, which only comes out at night and, for its size, has a large appetite. It feeds on the nectar, pollen and small insects found inside flowers, and has a most ingenious method of extracting its food.

When feeding, the honey-mouse makes its mouth into a kind of hollow tube, and its long tongue acts like a pump. This wonderful tongue, covered with fur and tipped with a brush of hairs, penetrates into the very heart of the flower.

So agile is this little honey-mouse, that sometimes it will catch insects in mid-flight in its human-like hands by leaping into the air after them.

The *planigale* is smaller even than the honey-mouse. Its rather flat head enables it to squeeze into incredibly tiny cracks. Crickets and grasshoppers are the planigale's staple diet, and quite often it will tackle a grasshopper as big as itself. Then, it overcomes its victim by clinging to it, and "riding" it relentlessly until the unfortunate grasshopper collapses and dies from sheer exhaustion.

And here to end with is the *wombat*, a very strange, tubby, dog-sized marsupial which, at one time, was found all over Australia.

In behaviour, the wombat is a typical rodent, feeding on grass, roots and other vegetable matter. Its burrow is a hundred feet long, and at the end of it, there are comfortable nests in spacious chambers.

The wombat looks rather like a small bear, and is an example of how marsupials have developed along lines more or less parallel to those of the normal un-pouched mammals of the rest of the world. Sadly, like so many other animals which at one time were found in great numbers, the wombat is becoming quite rare.

In a book of this size, it has been possible to describe only a few of the twelve thousand or so different species of living mammals. Yet, even among the ones we have looked at, there are far too many which will die out completely if something is not done to preserve their existence. It is for the sake of these and countless others that organisations like The World Wildlife Fund exist.

Those of us who have come to care about the welfare of animals, and to experience the thrill of stumbling across some weird creature whose way of life is fascinatingly different from anything we imagined, will be able to understand readily the tragedy of any one species becoming extinct.

It is possible that among the boys and girls who read this book and experience, perhaps for the first time, a sense of wonder at the marvellous diversity in the Animal Kingdom, there will be one or two who, in their turn, will venture forth into the wild places, in search of the rare and the unexpected.

On this last page then, I would dedicate this book to them—and to all who search in the hidden places—with no other purpose than to study and preserve and marvel at the strange and exotic creatures of our universe.

North American Opossum

Grey Kangaroo

Tiger

Noctule Bat

Beaver